CONTINUITY QUIZZES

First published in 2003 by Miles Kelly Publishing Ltd,
Bardfield Centre, Great Bardfield, Essex, CM7 4SL

Copyright © Miles Kelly Publishing Ltd 2003

ISBN 1-84236-281-X

2 4 6 8 10 9 7 5 3 1

Project Manager: Ruthie Boardman
Cover Design: Guy Rodgers

Contact us by email: info@mileskelly.net
Check our website and purchase other Miles Kelly products:
www.mileskelly.net

Printed in Italy

CONTINUITY QUIZZES

by
Christopher Rigby

Miles Kelly
PUBLISHING

About the Author

Born in Blackburn, Lancashire in 1960, Christopher Rigby
has been compiling and presenting pub quizzes for the past
15 years. When he is not adding to his material for quizzes,
Christopher works in the car industry. He is married to
Clare – they have two teenage daughters, Hollie and Ashley
and share their home with two demented dogs called Vespa
and Bailey. A keen Manchester United fan Christopher lists
his heroes as George Best and Homer Simpson.

CONTINUITY QUIZZES EXPLAINED

This quiz book comprises 90 general knowledge quizzes in which the answer to each question contains a word that is repeated in the answer to the next question.
Below are a few examples:

1. Which Time Lord battled against the Daleks?   (Dr Who)
2. Which 1976 film was based on a Rudyard Kipling novel and co-starred Sean Connery, Christopher Plummer and Michael Caine?   (The Man WHO Would Be King)
3. Which Beatles album cover featured the Fab Four walking across a zebra crossing?   (Abbey ROAD)

And so on with each answer up to No 10, repeating a word in the previous answer.

QUIZ ONE

1. Which Premiership football ground is located on Sir Matt Busby Way?

2. Which Dickens novel featured the character of Little Nell?

3. Which 80s pop band had hits with 'Down To Earth', 'Misfit' and 'Ordinary Day'?

4. Which Tennessee Williams play featured the character of Big Daddy and was adapted into a film in 1958 co-starring Paul Newman and Elizabeth Taylor?

5. Who did Jack Haley play in the 1939 version of *The Wizard of Oz*?

6. Which 1962 John Ford western co-starred James Stewart and John Wayne as the heroes and Lee Marvin as the villain of the piece?

7. What piece of music by John Sousa was used as the TV theme for *Monty Python's Flying Circus*?

8. Which inventor of the telephone provided the title of a hit record for the glam rock group Sweet?

9. Which leader from ancient times rode a horse called Bucephalus?

10. What began on September 2, 1666?

ANSWERS

1. Old Trafford 2. *The Old Curiosity Shop* 3. CURIOSITY Killed The Cat 4. CAT On A Hot Tin Roof 5. The TIN Man 6. *The MAN Who Shot Liberty Valance* 7. The LIBERTY Bell March 8. Alexander Graham BELL 9. ALEXANDER The Great 10. The GREAT Fire Of London

QUIZ TWO

1. In which 1984 film starring Eddie Murphy did Judge Reinhold play Detective Billy Rosewood?

2. How are Palatine, Aventine, Capitoline, Esquiline, Caeline, Viminal and Quirinal collectively known?

3. Which Disney animation featured the song, 'Whistle While You Work'?

4. Who is the editor of the *Daily Planet*?

5. Who plays the role of Chandler Bing in the sitcom *Friends*?

6. In the Bible, who are the four evangelists?

7. Who played the Bond girl Tiffany Case in the Bond film *Diamonds Are Forever*?

8. What is the capital of the island of Guernsey?

9. Who directed the film *Lord Of The Rings: Fellowship of the Ring* starring Ian McKellan and Elijah Wood?

10. Which 20th-century American abstract artist painted *Guardian Of The Secret* and *Moby Dick*?

ANSWERS
1. *Beverly Hills Cop* 2. The Seven HILLS of Rome 3. Snow White and The SEVEN Dwarves 4. Perry WHITE 5. Matthew PERRY 6. MATTHEW, Mark, Luke and John 7. Jill St JOHN 8. ST Peter Port 9. PETER Jackson 10. JACKSON Pollock

QUIZ THREE

1. Which horse made racing history by winning the Aintree Grand National in 1973, 1974 and 1977?

2. Which organisation was founded in Geneva in 1863 by Henri Dunant?

3. Who played the athlete Harold Abrahams in the film *Chariots Of Fire*?

4. In London, what was cast in April 1858 and weighs 13,760 kg?

5. In which 1970 film did Dustin Hoffman play an American Indian called Jack Crabb?

6. Which TV series set in Walnut Grove was based on the novel by Laura Ingalls Wilder?

7. Which members of the squirrel family live underground and have five different species called Black Tailed, White Tailed, Gunnison's, Utah and Mexican?

8. In which 1975 film did Al Pacino play a bank robber?

9. Who, appointed Poet Laureate in 1968, wrote detective stories under the name of Nicholas Blake?

10. Which film director with the middle name of Blount directed two versions of the Biblical epic *The Ten Commandments*, the second of which starred Charlton Heston as Moses?

ANSWERS

1. Red Rum 2. The International RED Cross 3. Ben CROSS 4. Big BEN 5. *Little BIG Man* 6. *LITTLE House On The Prairie* 7. PRAIRIE Dog 8. *DOG Day Afternoon* 9. Cecil DAY Lewis 10. CECIL B De Mille

QUIZ FOUR

1. Which American golfer is supported by a group of fans known as Arnie's Army?
2. Which rock trio with the first names of Keith, Greg and Carl had an instrumental hit with 'Fanfare For The Common Man'?
3. In Arthurian legend how is Vivien, who gave Arthur his sword Excalibur, more commonly known?
4. Which English monarch reigned for just nine days in 1553?
5. In which 1962 film did Bette Davis and Joan Crawford play sisters who lived together in an old Hollywood mansion?
6. How does Que Sera Sera translate into English?
7. Who played the Fresh Prince of Bel Air on TV before becoming a best-selling recording artist and a Hollywood superstar?
8. In which western TV series did Ben Murphy play Kid Curry?
9. What was the title of the second film that featured the all-action hero Indiana Jones?
10. What is the name of the building that is depicted on the flag of Cambodia?

QUIZ FIVE

1. What is the fourth book of The Old Testament?
2. What was the former name of the rock group The Who?
3. Which musical starring Grace Kelly was based on the film *The Philadelphia Story*?
4. What do the initials of the charity NSPCC stand for?
5. Which adventure novel penned by Captain Marryat was set in the year 1647?
6. What seven words open the Animals hit, 'House Of The Rising Sun'?
7. Which building on Pennsylvania Avenue was first occupied in 1800, eight years after construction began?
8. What beastly nickname was acquired by the golfer Greg Norman?
9. Who became Tsar of Russia in 1672 and introduced a tax for people with beards?
10. Which actor played the title role in the 1987 film *Robocop*?

ANSWERS
1. Numbers 2. The High NUMBERS 3. *HIGH Society* 4. National SOCIETY For Prevention Of Cruelty To Children 5. *CHILDREN OfThe New Forest* 6. There is a house in NEW Orleans 7. The White HOUSE 8. The Great WHITE Shark 9. Peter the GREAT 10. PETER Weller

QUIZ SIX

1. A labour is the collective noun for which burrowing animal?

2. In which best-selling novel did the adolescent creation of Sue Townsend first appear?

3. Which novel by Frances Hodgson Burnett told the story of a ten-year-old girl called Mary Lennox who lived with her parents in India?

4. In which Biblical paradise was Eve tempted by the serpent to eat the fruit from the tree of the knowledge of good and evil?

5. Who was British Prime Minister during the Suez Crisis of the 1950s?

6. Who did Richard Burton play in the 1963 film *Cleopatra*?

7. Who wrote the novel *The Prisoner Of Zenda*?

8. According to Christian belief, what are the three theological virtues?

9. Which 60s pop star was born Terence Nelhams?

10. Which 80s group had hits with 'Stand and Deliver' and 'Dog Eat Dog'?

QUIZ SEVEN

1. According to the legend who is said to have driven the snakes out of Ireland?

2. Who played the wife in the TV series *McMillan and Wife*?

3. Who provided the voice of Darth Vader in the *Star Wars* films?

4. Who recorded the album *Reload* on which he collaborated with several contemporary artists including Robbie Williams and The Stereophonics?

5. Which novel by Thomas Hughes first featured a bully called Flashman?

6. In which sitcom did the alien character of Mork first appear?

7. What are the names of the seven dwarves?

8. In which 1991 film comedy did Michael J Fox play a plastic surgeon?

9. Which 80s pop group took their name from a headline about Old Blue Eyes?

10. Who provided lead vocals for the pop group The Four Seasons?

QUIZ EIGHT

1. In which Brighton hotel were five members of the Conservative Party killed in 1984?
2. Which nursery rhyme character had 10,000 men under his command who he marched up and down a hill?
3. Where did the foodstuff chop suey originate?
4. What was the name of the parliamentary force that was formed in 1645 and initially commanded by Sir Thomas Fairfax?
5. In the TV series and film *MASH* what does the acronym MASH stand for?
6. What was founded in London in 1852 and is sometimes referred to by the acronym GOSH?
7. Which huge construction was commenced in 7 BC under the Zhou Dynasty?
8. On which Pink Floyd song did the Islington Green School Choir provide the backing vocals?
9. Which song from the musical *Evita* begins with the line, 'I don't expect my love affairs to last for long'?
10. Which London building opened in 1871 and was dedicated to the late husband of Queen Victoria?

ANSWERS

1. The Grand Hotel 2. The GRAND Old Duke of York 3. New YORK 4. NEW Model Army 5. Mobile ARMY Surgical Hospital 6. Great Ormond Street HOSPITAL 7. The GREAT Wall of China 8. 'Another Brick in The WALL.' 9. 'ANOTHER Suitcase ANOTHER Hall' 10. Albert HALL.

QUIZ NINE

1. Nadia Comaneci was the first gymnast to score a perfect 10. Who was the second to achieve this feat?

2. Who followed in her father's pop music footsteps with her first hit 'Kids In America' in 1981?

3. Who was born in 1854, died in 1900 and was played on film by Stephen Fry in 1997?

4. Which slobbish character was played by Jack Klugman in the TV series *The Odd Couple*?

5. 2, Pennsylvania Plaza is the official address of which New York theatre and sports venue?

6. In 1991, from where in Moscow was Lenin's statue removed?

7. From which club did the New York Yankees purchase the baseball star Babe Ruth?

8. Which historical protest against taxes took place in Massachusetts in 1773?

9. Which political organisation was founded by Screaming Lord Sutch and has its headquarters at the Dog and Partridge public house in Hampshire?

10. What is the name of the brightly coloured venomous lizard that was named after the river basin in the USA where it is commonly found?

QUIZ TEN

1. Who was born in Dublin in 1856, was a co-founder of the Fabian Society and wrote the plays *Candida* and *Heartbreak House*?

2. Which golfer was captain of Europe's triumphant Ryder Cup team in 1995?

3. Which pop star brother married and divorced Meg Matthews?

4. Reputedly whose last words were, 'Goodnight my darlings, I'll see you tomorrow'?

5. Which Kenny Rogers hit song contains the line, 'It don't mean you're weak if you turn the other cheek'?

6. Which football club moved from the Baseball Ground to Pride Park?

7. Which horse race is held at Churchill Downs in the USA and was first won in 1875 by a horse called Aristides?

8. What do the initials KFC stand for with regard to the fast food chain?

9. In which Nick Park animated film did Jane Horrocks provide the voice of Ginger?

10. What is the name of the winter sport course that runs from St Moritz to the village of Celerina?

ANSWERS

1. George Bernard Shaw 2. BERNARD Gallagher 3. Noel GALLAGHER 4. NOEL Coward 5. 'COWARD Of The County' 6. Derby COUNTY 7. Kentucky DERBY 8. KENTUCKY Fried Chicken 9. *CHICKEN Run* 10. The Cresta RUN

QUIZ ONE

1. Which scientist was born in Stockholm in 1833 and in 1875 produced the first gelignite?

2. What award connects Lech Walesa, Nelson Mandela, Desmond Tutu, Mother Teresa, Amnesty International and Martin Luther King?

3. Natasha is the name of the heroine in which epic novel by Leo Tolstoy set during the Napoleonic War?

4. In which war was the Battle of Ia Drang Valley fought?

5. In which film did Robin Williams play a DJ called Adrian Cronauer, a role that earned him his first Oscar nomination?

6. Which novel by Louisa May Alcott opens with the line, 'In order that we may start afresh and go to Meg's wedding with free minds, it will be well to begin with a little gossip about the Marches'?

7. What is the only Shakespeare play that contains a British place name in the title?

8. Which building was badly damaged by fire on November 20, 1992?

9. Name the female politician who died in 2002 and was responsible for introducing the Breathalyser when she was Minister for Transport.

10. Which two singers duetted on the song 'I Know Him So Well' in the 1985 charts?

ANSWERS

1. Alfred Nobel 2. NOBEL Peace Prize 3. *War And PEACE* 4. The Vietnam WAR 5. *Good Morning VIETNAM* 6. *GOOD Wives* 7. *The Merry WIVES Of Windsor* 8. WINDSOR Castle 9. Barbara CASTLE 10. Elaine Paige and BARBRA Dickson

QUIZ TWO

1. Which peak that stands 1086 m high overlooks the city of Cape Town?

2. Which order did King Arthur establish for his trusted companions in 516 AD?

3. What was the name of the monastic military order established at the end of the First Crusade to protect Christian pilgrims on their travels to the Holy Land?

4. Which literary creation of Leslie Charteris is also known as The Saint?

5. Name the ex-husband of Carrie Fisher who had a 1986 hit with 'You Can Call Me Al'?

6. Which folk trio known by their first names had a 1970 hit with 'Leaving On A Jet Plane'?

7. Name the four entertainers who made up The Goons.

8. What was the name of the spiv character played by George Cole in the St Trinians films?

9. Dale Arden was the female companion of which superhero?

10. What is the real name of the pop star Sting?

QUIZ THREE

1. Which album by the pop group Queen featured the classic track 'Bohemian Rhapsody'?
2. Which 1978 film featured the Bee Gees song 'How Deep Is Your Love'?
3. Which viral disease is passed to humans via mosquitoes and causes jaundice of the skin?
4. What is worn by the leader of the Tour de France?
5. Trenton is the capital of which US state?
6. According to the Eagles who was Johnny-come-lately?
7. Who did John Wayne play in the film *Stagecoach*?
8. Who married Barbara Bach and co-starred with her in the film *Caveman*?
9. Which Nashville-born singer had hits with the songs 'War' and 'Contact'?
10. Who sculpted the lions at the base of Nelson's Column in Trafalgar Square?

QUIZ FOUR

1. What was the second film to feature the character of Luke Skywalker?
2. What do the initials BEM stand for with regard to awards?
3. What was the former name of Kenya?
4. Which Oscar-winning film chronicled the life of Karen Blixen?
5. Which book by George Orwell tells of the time he spent amongst the poor in the capitals of France and England?
6. Who wrote the novel *White Fang*?
7. Who played the Artful Dodger in the Oscar-winning musical *Oliver*?
8. In which 1999 film did Will Smith play the hero and Kenneth Branagh play the villain?
9. In which US state did the Charleston dance originate?
10. Who won the Women's Singles at Wimbledon in the Queen's Silver Jubilee year?

ANSWERS

1. *The Empire Strikes Back* 2. British EMPIRE Medal 3. BRITISH East Africa 4. *Out Of AFRICA* 5. *Down And OUT In Paris And London* 6. Jack LONDON 7. JACK Wild 8. WILD WILD West 9. WEST Virginia 10. VIRGINIA Wade

QUIZ FIVE

1. Who wears a signet ring known as The Fisherman's Ring?

2. In which 1984 film did Mickey Rourke and Eric Roberts play two cousins called Charlie and Paulie?

3. What do the initials GMT stand for?

4. Which novel by HG Wells was filmed in 1960 with Rod Taylor and was remade in 2002 with Guy Pearce?

5. For which group did Gloria Estefan provide lead vocals on the hit record 'Dr Beat'?

6. Which Oscar-winning film of 1965 was directed by Robert Wise?

7. Which show features the songs 'Lida Rose' and '76 Trombones'?

8. Which play by Robert Bolt told the story of Sir Thomas More?

9. What is the collective name for the quartet of violin concertos composed by Antonio Vivaldi in 1725?

10. Which Sherlock Holmes story opens with a chapter called The Science Of Deduction?

ANSWERS

1. The Pope 2. The POPE Of Greenwich Village 3. GREENWICH Mean Time 4. The TIME Machine 5. Miami Sound MACHINE 6. The SOUND Of Music 7. The MUSIC Man 8. A MAN For All Seasons 9. The Four SEASONS 10. The Sign Of FOUR

QUIZ SIX

1. Who led the peasant's revolt against Richard II in 1381?
2. Which entertainer formed her own production company called MTM Productions?
3. Name the English and American actors who played the title roles in the 70s TV series *The Persuaders*.
4. Who replaced John Smith as leader of the Labour Party?
5. Which 1999 film shot with hand-held cameras co-starred Heather Donahue and Joshua Leonard?
6. Peter, Susan, Lucy and Edmond are four of the main characters in which fantasy novel by CS Lewis?
7. In which film did Rowan Atkinson provide the voice of Zazu?
8. In 1964, who became the youngest-ever recipient of a Nobel Peace Prize?
9. Which entertainer is the mother of the actor Larry Hagman?
10. Which novel by Charles Dickens featured the character of Sarah Gamp?

ANSWERS

1. Wat Tyler 2. Mary TYLER Moore 3. Roger MOORE and Tony Curtis 4. TONY Blair 5. The BLAIR Witch Project 6. The Lion, The WITCH and The Wardrobe 7. The LION King 8. Martin Luther KING 9. Mary MARTIN 10. MARTIN Chuzzlewit

QUIZ SEVEN

1. Which song about a wedding ring was the biggest hit of the singer Freda Payne?
2. Which best-selling book by Stephen E Ambrose chronicled events in World War II and was adapted into a mini TV series starring Tom Hanks and Dexter Fletcher?
3. Which quintet starred in the films *Duck Soup* and *A Day At The Races*?
4. Which Chicago-born singer had hits with the songs 'Hazard' and 'Right Here Waiting'?
5. The nursery rhyme character of Humpty Dumpty was inspired by which English monarch?
6. Which award-winning TV sitcom features the alien character of Dick Solomon?
7. What is the state capital of Arkansas?
8. At which battle was General Custer defeated by the combined forces of Sitting Bull and Crazy Horse?
9. What is the name of the historical event at which William the Conqueror was triumphant on the site of Senlac Hill?
10. In 1964, who became the leader of Malawi?

ANSWERS

1.'Band Of Gold'. 2. *BAND Of Brothers* 3. The Marx BROTHERS 4. Richard MARX 5. RICHARD The Third 6. *THIRD Rock From The Sun* 7. Little ROCK 8. The Battle of the LITTLE Big Horn 9. The BATTLE Of Hastings 10. HASTINGS Banda

QUIZ EIGHT

1. Which novel was Charles Dickens writing at the time of his death?
2. In the cartoon series *Scooby Doo* what words were written on the side of the van occupied by the ghost hunters?
3. In which 1974 film did Burt Reynolds play a fallen American football star that was jailed for drunkenness and car theft?
4. Which album by the pop group The Police contained the tracks 'Spirits In The Material World' and 'Every Little Thing She Does Is Magic'?
5. Which classic film of 1947 starred Rex Harrison and told the story of a widow who fell in love with the ghost of a sea captain?
6. Which Simon and Garfunkel hit contains the line, 'Where have you gone Joe DiMaggio, a nation turns its lonely eyes to you'?
7. Fritz, Ernest, Franz and Jack are the lead characters in which novel by J Wyss?
8. Shirley Jones and David Cassidy were both members of which 1970s pop group?
9. What did my true love give to me on the first day of Christmas?
10. Which song opens with the line, 'I'm coming home I've done my time'?

QUIZ NINE

1. What is the name of the dead business partner of Ebenezer Scrooge?
2. Which reggae legend was backed by the Wailers?
3. Which actor star of the 2001 film *Monster's Ball* married fellow thespian Angelina Jolie in May 2000?
4. In which film did Julie Walters play the ballet instructor of Jamie Bell?
5. What was the title of the BBC drama series that starred Jean Marsh and told the true story of two sisters who owned a 1920s fashion house?
6. In which 1999 horror movie were five people invited to occupy the house of a wealthy eccentric played by Geoffrey Rush?
7. Which major battle of the American War of Independence was fought on June 16, 1775?
8. What is the title of the final novel in the Narnia chronicles by C S Lewis?
9. What was the original title of the George Orwell novel *1984*?
10. In which 1976 film did David Bowie play an alien who visited Earth in search of water?

QUIZ TEN

1. What is the title of the 2002 film, the fifth in the *Star Wars* series?

2. Which album by Queen contains the tracks 'Killer Queen', 'Now I'm Here' and 'Flick Of The Wrist'?

3. The film *Apocalypse Now* was based on which Joseph Conrad novel?

4. What are the first five words in the lyrics of the song 'The Sound Of Silence'?

5. What is the first property on a London Monopoly board?

6. Which Catholic priest became Chairperson for CND (Campaign For Nuclear Disarmament)?

7. Who was King of Scotland from 1306 to 1329?

8. Who played the secret agent Napoleon Solo in *The Man From UNCLE*?

9. Which 20th-century musician composed *The Sea Symphony*?

10. Who won the Women's Singles in the 1999 US Open at tennis?

ANSWERS

1. *The Attack Of The Clones* 2. *Sheer Heart ATTACK* 3. HEART *Of Darkness* 4. Hello DARKNESS my old friend 5. OLD Kent Road 6. Bruce KENT 7. Robert the BRUCE 8. ROBERT Vaughn 9. VAUGHN Williams 10. Serena WILLIAMS

QUIZ ONE

1. Which 1982 film co-directed by Frank Oz and Jim Henson featured mythical races of creatures called Urskeks and Mystics?
2. Who connects the films *City Slickers* and *When Harry Met Sally*?
3. Which singer had his biggest hit in 1974 with the song 'I Can Help'?
4. Which Tchaikovsky ballet tells the story of a princess called Odette?
5. What covers an area of 67,850 sq km and is the main reservoir of the River Nile?
6. Which British national museum of art and design is sometimes referred to by the initials V & A?
7. Who played Hercule Poirot in the 1974 film version of *Murder On The Orient Express*?
8. Which football star of yesteryear was nicknamed The Preston Plumber?
9. Which novel by Henry Fielding was adapted into an Oscar-winning film in 1963?
10. What is the name of New York's stock exchange?

ANSWERS
1. *The Dark Crystal* 2. Billy CRYSTAL 3. BILLY Swan 4. *SWAN Lake* 5. LAKE Victoria 6. VICTORIA & Albert 7. ALBERT Finney 8. Tom FINNEY 9. *TOM Jones* 10. The Dow JONES Index

QUIZ TWO

1. Which novel by Muriel Spark was set in the Marcia Blaine School for Girls?
2. What title was won by 18-year-old Agbani Darego in 2001?
3. Which novel by Jules Verne featured the characters of Passepartout and Mrs Aouda?
4. What was the title of the 1975 film in which Robert Redford played a CIA researcher called Joe Turner?
5. Which story by Jerome K Jerome featured a dog called Montmorency?
6. Which TV series of the 1970s centred around events on a cruise liner called the *Pacific Princess*?
7. What does the Latin phrase *Amor vincit omnia* mean in English?
8. What is the seven word motto of the Three Musketeers?
9. In which novel by Ernest Hemingway did the character of Robert Jordan fight for the Loyalists in the Spanish Civil War?
10. What is rung at the Lloyds Building in times of disaster?

ANSWERS

1. *The Prime of Miss Jean Brodie* 2. MISS World 3. Around *The WORLD In Eighty Days* 4. *Three DAYS Of The Condor* 5. *THREE Men In A Boat* 6. *The Love BOAT* 7. LOVE conquers all 8. ALL for one, and one for all 9. FOR Whom *The Bell Tolls* 10. The Lutine BELL

27

3

QUIZ THREE

1. Which spaceship was captained by James T Kirk?
2. What sank on March 6, 1987?
3. Which 1995 film sequel was sub-titled The Adventure Home?
4. Which 1971 film based on a Roald Dahl story starred Gene Wilder as the owner of a factory?
5. The song 'You Sexy Thing' that featured in the film *The Full Monty* was a hit for which pop group?
6. Which 1959 film was directed by Billy Wilder and co-starred Marilyn Monroe, Jack Lemmon and Tony Curtis?
7. Which Madonna hit starts with the line, 'I made it through the wilderness'?
8. Which Leslie Thomas novel about an Asian military base featured the character of Private Brigg?
9. Which rousing hymn was composed by Arthur S Sullivan and was sung at the end of the Oscar-winning film *Mrs Miniver*?
10. Who has been played on film by Mel Gibson and Marlon Brando?

ANSWERS

1. USS *Enterprise* 2. *The Herald Of Free ENTERPRISE* 3. *FREE Willy II* 4. *WILLY Wonka And The Chocolate Factory* 5. Hot CHOCOLATE 6. *Some Like It HOT* 7. 'LIKE A Virgin' 8. *The VIRGIN Soldiers* 9. 'Onward Christian SOLDIERS' 10. Fletcher CHRISTIAN

28

QUIZ FOUR

1. How were Jill, Sabrina and Kelly collectively known in the title of a popular TV series of the 1970s?
2. In which classic 1930s film did James Cagney play a hoodlum called Rocky Sullivan?
3. What was the title of the first film in which Clint Eastwood played Inspector Callahan?
4. What was the third novel by JK Rowling that was set at Hogwarts School?
5. Which Australian TV drama was set at the Wentworth Detention Centre?
6. Jordan Knight, Jonathan Knight, Donnie Wahlberg, Joe McIntyre and Danny Wood were the five members of which boy band?
7. In which Australian state is the city of Sydney?
8. What is the title of the cartoon series that is set in Colorado and features the characters of Chef and Kenny?
9. What was acquired by Henry VIII in 1536, having been previously owned by the monks of Westminster Abbey?
10. Which novel published in 1886 featured a butler called Poole and a lawyer called Utterson?

ANSWERS

1. *Charlie's Angels* 2. ANGELS With Dirty Faces 3. DIRTY Harry 4. HARRY Potter And The *Prisoner of Azkaban* 5. PRISONER Cell Block H 6. New Kids On The BLOCK 7. NEW South Wales 8. SOUTH Park 9. Hyde PARK 10. *The Strange Case Of Dr Jekyll And Mr HYDE*

QUIZ FIVE

1. Which singer was born Nathaniel Adams?

2. Which cartoon series features a married couple called Hank and Peggy who have a son called Bobby?

3. In which award-winning police TV drama did Veronica Hamel play Joyce Davenport?

4. What is the name of the thoroughfare on which Heartbreak Hotel is situated?

5. Which 1960s pop album included the songs 'She's Leaving Home' and 'Lucy In The Sky With Diamonds'?

6. Who says, 'Off with her head' in *Alice's Adventures In Wonderland*?

7. Which monarch knighted Isaac Newton?

8. Which book tells the story of a thirteen-year-old Jewish girl and her family whom the Germans force into hiding during World War II?

9. Which TV detective was played by William Conrad from 1971 to 1976?

10. Name the comedy duo that starred in the film *The Boys In Blue*.

ANSWERS

1. Nat King Cole 2. KING Of The Hill 3. HILL Street Blues 4. Lonely STREET 5. Sergeant Peppers LONELY Hearts Club Band 6. Queen Of HEARTS 7. QUEEN Anne 8. The Diary of ANNE Frank 9. FRANK Cannon 10. CANNON And Ball

QUIZ SIX

1. In which sitcom did Will Smith play a rapper who left Philadelphia to live with wealthy relatives?
2. Who did Flora McDonald help to escape to the Isle of Skye?
3. Who appeared as himself singing 'Behind Closed Doors' in the film *Every Which Way But Loose*?
4. Which novel by Irwin Shaw told the story of the Jordache family?
5. In which film is the lead villain called Scaramanga?
6. The building of what was completed in May 1937 in San Francisco?
7. Which film recounted the true story of the 1944 Battle of Arnhem?
8. Bathsheba Everdene is the heroine of which Thomas Hardy novel?
9. What was the title of The Beatles, first ever No 1 hit single in the UK?
10. In which 2000 film did Jim Carrey play a character suffering from schizophrenia?

QUIZ SEVEN

1. The first permanent stands at which Hong Kong racecourse were built in 1931?
2. Which song from the musical *South Pacific* provided a 1982 hit for Captain Sensible?
3. Which song from the film *Dr Doolittle* won a Best Song Oscar?
4. What was the title of the novel by Gerald Durrell that featured a pigeon called Quasimodo and an owl called Ulysses?
5. What song provided the biggest hit for the pop group Traffic in 1967?
6. In which prison were 146 prisoners held in 1756 under the orders of the Nawab of Bengal?
7. Richard Shenton is the hero of which Robert Louis Stevenson novel set during The War Of The Roses?
8. Which 1996 film sees Christian Slater as the hero battling against a villain played by John Travolta?
9. Which hit for Jimmy Ruffin opens with the line, 'As I walk this land with broken dreams, I have visions of many things'?
10. What was the first novel by Susan Coolidge that featured the schoolgirl Katy Carr?

ANSWERS

1. Happy Valley 2. 'HAPPY Talk' 3. 'TALK To The Animals' 4. *My Family And Other ANIMALS* 5. 'Hole In MY Shoe' 6. Black HOLE Of Calcutta 7. *BLACK Arrow* 8. *Broken ARROW* 9. 'What Becomes Of The BROKEN Hearted' 10. *WHAT Katy Did*

QUIZ EIGHT

1. Which Shakespeare play contains the line, 'The better part of valour is discretion'?

2. Which former member of The Drifters had a solo hit with the song 'Stand By Me'?

3. Which comedian wrote the novels *Gridlock* and *Stark*?

4. Who recorded the albums *Too Low For Zero* and *Don't Shoot Me I'm Only The Piano Player*?

5. Which former leader of the Labour Party is buried on the island of Iona?

6. Who was the first professional boxer to inflict a defeat on Frank Bruno?

7. Which movie icon died in a car crash in California in 1955?

8. When Teri Hatcher plays Lois Lane, who plays Superman?

9. Who were the first two births recorded in the Bible?

10. In the Dickens novel *Great Expectations,* what is the name of the escaped convict?

ANSWERS
1. *King Henry IV Part 1* 2. Ben E KING 3. BEN Elton 4. ELTON John 5. JOHN Smith
6. James Bonecrusher SMITH 7. JAMES Dean 8. DEAN Cain 9. CAIN & Abel 10. ABEL
Magwitch

QUIZ NINE

1. Which poem by Tennyson contains the line, 'All in the valley of death rode the six hundred'?
2. Jeff Lynne provided lead vocals for which pop group that recorded the hit album *Out Of The Blue*?
3. Where was Eddy Grant 'gonna rock down to' in a 1983 hit record?
4. Which thoroughfare is the centre of New York's advertising industry?
5. Which novel by Robert James Waller was adapted into a film starring Clint Eastwood and Meryl Streep?
6. Which actor who starred in the films *Airplane* and *High Noon* was followed into the film industry by his sons Beau and Jeff?
7. Who was Prime Minister of Great Britain from 1916 to 1922?
8. Which actor is synonymous with the role of Arthur Daley?
9. Name the singer born in 1950 who had hits with 'Pink Cadillac' and 'Miss You Like Crazy'?
10. Which star of the films *Rebel Without A Cause* and *West Side Story* died in 1981 in tragic circumstances?

ANSWERS
1. *The Charge Of The Light Brigade* 2. Electric LIGHT Orchestra 3. ELECTRIC Avenue 4. Madison AVENUE 5. *The Bridges of MADISON County* 6. Lloyd BRIDGES 7. David LLOYD George 8. GEORGE Cole 9. Natalie COLE 10. NATALIE Wood

QUIZ TEN

1. In which film comedy did Robert De Niro subject Ben Stiller to a lie detector test?

2. What was the title of the 1998 film in which Brad Pitt played a personification of death?

3. Robert Palmer and Elkie Brooks were both members of which 70s pop group?

4. What are the more common names for sodium chloride and acetic acid?

5. In which city in the state of Utah is the headquarters of the Mormon religion?

6. According to the Christmas hymn, where did a lowly cattle shed once stand?

7. Which organisation's motto is, 'Let Not The Deep Swallow Me Up'?

8. Which Enid Bagnold novel was adapted into a film starring Elizabeth Taylor and Mickey Rooney?

9. What was the title of the 1986 cult movie directed by David Lynch and starring Dennis Hopper as a deranged kidnapper?

10. Which painting by Thomas Gainsborough was the portrait of a youngster called Jonathan Buttall?

SESSION 4

QUIZ ONE

1. Which actress born in 1979 is the daughter of Goldie Hawn?
2. Which Cole Porter musical features the songs 'Wunderbar' and 'So In Love'?
3. For which 1985 film did William Hurt win a Best Actor Oscar?
4. Diana Prince is the secret identity of which super heroine?
5. Which Elvis Presley hit opens with the line, 'When no one else can understand me'?
6. What do the initials WYSIWYG stand for with regard to computer terminology?
7. Which 1971 film starring Michael Caine was based on the Ted Lewis novel *Jack's Return Home*?
8. Who is the only President of the USA to be born in the state of Georgia?
9. Who won his first Wimbledon Singles title in 1974?
10. In the classic TV western series who played the title role in *The Rifleman*?

QUIZ TWO

1. In the human body, what is the more common name for the ulna nerve?
2. Which 1968 musical starred Barbara Streisand as Fanny Brice?
3. In which TV series did Stephanie Powers play April Dancer?
4. What was the title of the film in which Macauley Culkin played the nephew of John Candy?
5. Which sci-fi TV series featured the characters of Princess Ardala and a robot called Twiki?
6. The 1963 film *Cleopatra* almost caused the bankruptcy of which film company that was founded in 1915?
7. Who founded the religious group known as the Quakers?
8. In which 1994 film did Helen Mirren play Queen Charlotte?
9. Which movie monster scaled the Empire State Building whilst keeping a firm grip on Fay Wray?
10. What was the last road film made by Bob Hope and Bing Crosby?

ANSWERS

1. The funny bone 2. FUNNY Girl 3. The GIRL From Uncle 4. UNCLE Buck 5. BUCK Rogers In The 25th Century 6. 20th CENTURY Fox 7. George FOX 8. The Madness Of King GEORGE 9. KING Kong 10. The Road To Hong KONG

QUIZ THREE

1. What was the title of the adventure starring Wallace and Gromit in which the intrepid duo enjoyed a trip to the moon?

2. What waterway travels for 1771 km from Beijing to Hangzhou?

3. What, measuring 63 km in length, was opened by Queen Victoria in 1894?

4. Which football team was originally called Ardwick FC?

5. What is the state capital of Missouri?

6. Who was the third President of the USA?

7. Which knighted man of the cloth was executed on July 6, 1535 on the orders of King Henry VIII?

8. In which 1967 film did Sydney Poitier play a teacher and Lulu play a pupil?

9. What novel by Eric Segal was filmed in 1970 and featured the character of Oliver Barrett IV?

10. Which novel by Michael Ende is set in the mystical realms of Fantasia and features a youthful hero called Bastion?

ANSWERS

1. A Grand Day Out 2. GRAND Canal 3. Manchester Ship CANAL 4. MANCHESTER City 5. Jefferson CITY 6. Thomas JEFFERSON 7. Sir THOMAS More 8. To SIR With Love 9. LOVE Story 10. The Never Ending STORY

QUIZ FOUR

1. What is the four-letter name of the alcoholic drink distilled from honey and water?
2. Which village is the home of Miss Marple?
3. Who connects the films *Thoroughly Modern Millie* and *Ordinary People*?
4. At the age of 23, who became the youngest-ever player to captain England's football team and went on to win 108 international caps?
5. Who married Whitney Houston in 1992?
6. Of what did The Rolling Stones ask, 'How come you taste so good'?
7. According to the nursery rhyme, what are little girls made of?
8. Which group released an album entitled *Forever* in 2000?
9. Which sitcom co-starring Tracey Ullman, Jennifer Saunders, Dawn French and Ruby Wax was first shown on TV in 1985?
10. Ice, Maverick, Viper and Goose are all characters in which 1986 film blockbuster?

ANSWERS
1. Mead 2. St Mary MEAD 3. MARY Tyler Moore 4. Bobby MOORE 5. BOBBY Brown 6. BROWN Sugar 7. SUGAR and spice and all things nice 8. The SPICE Girls 9. GIRLS On Top 10. TOP Gun

QUIZ FIVE

1. Which 1963 Disney film told the true story of two dogs and a cat and their trek across Canada to find their family?

2. Which 1864 adventure novel by Jules Verne featured the character of Professor Lidenbrock?

3. What song was a 1987 chart-topper for Belinda Carlisle?

4. Which 1951 film starring Shelley Winters was nominated for nine Oscars and was based on the 1925 novel *An American Tragedy*?

5. Which novel by JG Ballard recounted his childhood in a Japanese prisoner of war camp?

6. In New York, what has 73 elevators, 6500 windows and became the world's tallest building on its completion in 1931?

7. Which former province of South Africa was sometimes abbreviated to OFS?

8. In the video for which 1984 hit did Freddie Mercury of Queen dress up in a black leather mini skirt?

9. What was The Beatles' first No 1 hit in the USA?

10. Which six words, also the title of a film, precede the saying that ends with 'rules the world'?

QUIZ SIX

1. Which story features the characters of Kaa and Mowgli?

2. What was the title of the 1997 Tarzan spoof in which Brendan Fraser plays the ape-man?

3. Which pop star released the albums *Faith*, *Older* and *Listen Without Prejudice*?

4. On film who has played Batman and Beetlejuice?

5. Which silent movie star was nicknamed The Great Stone Face?

6. Who was the first boxer to beat Mike Tyson in a pro fight?

7. Who won a Best Actor Oscar for the film *Wall Street*?

8. Who created the character of Paddington Bear?

9. Which fictional character was briefly married to Tracey Draco?

10. Who created the character of Detective Inspector Adam Dalgliesh?

QUIZ SEVEN

1. What is the world's largest amphibian?
2. What do the initials BFG stand for with regard to the Roald Dahl novel?
3. What was the title of the film in which Bette Midler and Lily Tomlin played sets of identical twins that were accidentally switched at birth?
4. What do the initials of the computer language COBOL stand for?
5. Which song, originally a hit in 1970 for Nicky Thomas, was covered by Paul Young in 1983?
6. Which D H Lawrence novel published in 1921 tells the story of two sisters called Ursula and Gudrun Brangwen?
7. What is the title of the novel by Louisa May Alcott that first introduces the March family?
8. Which musical features a man-eating plant called Audrey II?
9. How are Chris Lowe and Neil Tennant collectively known in the world of pop music?
10. Which musical is based on the Shakespeare play *The Comedy Of Errors*?

QUIZ EIGHT

1. Which novel by Fredrick Forsythe told the story of the attempted assassination of Charles De Gaulle?

2. What was Michael Jackson's first No 1 single in the UK?

3. To a golfer, what is an ace?

4. George Flat Nose Currie, the Logan Brothers and Butch Cassidy were all members of which band of outlaws?

5. What occurred on October 24, 1929 that shook the economic world?

6. Which long-running TV series is set in the Manchester borough of Weatherfield?

7. For which event were TV cameras first allowed to film inside Westminster Abbey?

8. Which Quaker woman was born in 1780, died in 1845 and devoted her life to reform the prison system in Britain?

9. Who played Peter in the 1992 film *Peter's Friends*?

10. Which Edinburgh-born snooker star became Scottish champion in 1986 when he was just 17 years of age?

QUIZ NINE

1. Who did Lee Major play in *The Six Million Dollar Man*?

2. Who played the husband of Diane Keaton in the 1991 film *Father Of The Bride*?

3. Who boxed under the name of Kid Sheleen before singing his way to stardom?

4. Where in England is there a sculpture trail that features pieces called Heart of Stone and Black Dome?

5. Which British football club won the 1979 European Cup courtesy of a single goal by Trevor Francis?

6. Who has been played on film many times including portrayals by Scott Brown, Alan Rickman and Melville Cooper?

7. Which lawman of the Wild West was shot and killed by Wayne Brazel in March, 1908?

8. Who played Elsie Tanner in *Coronation Street*?

9. Who played the young Indiana Jones in the film *Indiana Jones And The Last Crusade*?

10. Which World War II battle was fought in Uruguayan waters between Germany and Britain and ended with the scuttling of the German battleship *Graf Spee*?

QUIZ TEN

1. Who played the character of Don Lockwood in the film *Singing In The Rain*?

2. Which rock and roller noted for wearing black leather on stage had hits with 'Blue Jean Bop' and 'Be- Bop- A-Lula'?

3. Who painted *The Potato Eaters*?

4. Who played the bad in the film *The Good, The Bad And The Ugly*?

5. Who, born in 1807, was known as The Beloved General Of The South during the US Civil War?

6. Who played Toby Wren in the TV series *Doomwatch* and the Son of God in the TV production of *Jesus of Nazareth*?

7. In the first decade of the 20th century who received a knighthood from Edward VII and founded the Boy Scout movement?

8. In which novel by Frances Hodgson Burnett is the lead character called Cedric Errol?

9. In which film did Jane Horrocks impersonate Shirley Bassey and Barbara Streisand?

10. What do the initials HMV stand for with regard to the record label?

ANSWERS
1. Gene Kelly 2. GENE Vincent 3. VINCENT Van Gogh 4. Lee VAN Cleef 5. Robert E LEE 6. ROBERT Powell 7. Lord Baden POWELL 8. *Little LORD Fauntleroy* 9. *LITTLE Voice* 10. His Masters VOICE

QUIZ ONE

1. Which pop star topped the charts with 'Sailing' and 'Maggie May'?
2. What is the name of the parliamentary official who summons the House of Commons to hear the Queen's speech?
3. Bulgaria, Turkey and Romania all form a coastline with what?
4. Which novel by Ernest Hemingway won the Nobel Prize for Literature and told the story of an aging fisherman called Santiago?
5. In which film did Susan Sarandon play Sister Helen Prejean?
6. In which film did Robin Williams play Professor John Keating?
7. What do the initials RSPB stand for?
8. In the literary world what do the initials RSC stand for?
9. In which film did Joseph Fiennes play the Bard of Avon?
10. What was the first chart hit for The Beatles?

ANSWERS

1. Rod Stewart 2. Black ROD 3. BLACK Sea 4. The Old Man And The SEA 5. Dead MAN Walking 6. DEAD Poets Society 7. Royal SOCIETY For Protection Of Birds 8. ROYAL Shakespeare Company 9. SHAKESPEARE In Love 10. 'LOVE Me Do'.

QUIZ TWO

1. According to the nursery rhyme, what is Thursday's Child?
2. Which song mentions Marlene Dietrich, Picasso, the Aga Khan and the Rolling Stones in the lyrics?
3. Which TV drama is set in the town of Skelthwaite?
4. What song was No 1 for the Eurythmics in 1985?
5. What is the name of the 20-metre-high statue sculpted by Antony Gormley, which stands just outside the town of Gateshead?
6. Which US colonel retired in 1988 to defend himself against a special prosecution investigating events in Central America?
7. Who was born in the state of Georgia in 1892 and went on to star in the films *Way Out West* and *Another Fine Mess*?
8. Who wrote the novel *Jude The Obscure*?
9. Which inventor was nicknamed The Wizard of Menlo Park?
10. Tony Burrows provided lead vocals for which 70s pop group?

ANSWERS

1. Far to go 2. 'Where Do You Go To My Lovely' 3. WHERE *The Heart Is* 4. 'There Must Be An Angel Playing With My HEART' 5. ANGEL Of The North 6. Oliver NORTH 7. OLIVER Hardy 8. Thomas HARDY 9. THOMAS Alva Edison 10. EDISON Lighthouse

QUIZ THREE

1. What is the name of the snail in *The Magic Roundabout*?
2. Which member of The Rolling Stones died in July 1969?
3. Who played the Bond girl May Day in a 1985 film?
4. Which song associated with Scotland contains the line, 'I once was lost but now am found'?
5. What was the title of the 1972 film directed by Lionel Jeffries and based on a novel by Antonia Barber entitled *The Ghosts*?
6. Which James Hilton novel told the story of a teacher at a public school called Brookfield?
7. The film musical *Cabaret* was based on which novel by Christopher Isherwood?
8. What was the title of the second film that featured the spy character of Harry Palmer?
9. In 1965 Winston Churchill became the first commoner to be granted a what?
10. In which film did Will Smith play an attorney called Robert Clayton Dean who is framed for murder?

QUIZ FOUR

1. Which story about a teenager with telekinetic powers was the first Stephen King novel to be filmed?

2. Name the daughter of Debbie Reynolds who was born in 1956?

3. What was the title of the 1991 film in which Jeff Bridges starred as a DJ called Jack Lucas?

4. Who beat Bobby Riggs in a tennis match that was dubbed The Battle Of The Sexes?

5. What name was Marilyn Monroe born with?

6. Who played Lieutenant John Chard in the 1964 film *Zulu*?

7. What is the capital of the Falkland Islands?

8. What is the capital of Haiti?

9. What nickname was bestowed upon the eldest son of Edward III after he fought in the Battle of Crecy?

10. Which rock group recorded the albums *Paranoid* and *Sabotage*?

QUIZ FIVE

1. Who played Miss Moneypenny for the last time in *A View To A Kill*?
2. Who has been played on TV by a Hatcher and on film by a Kidder?
3. On which London thoroughfare does the Dorchester Hotel stand?
4. Which horseracing course stands 25 km South-east of Glasgow?
5. Who played the vampire in the comedy film *Love At First Bite*?
6. Which Irish-born playwright won the Nobel Prize for Literature in 1925?
7. Who played the captain of the *Titanic* in the 1997 film?
8. Who was Formula One World Champion in 1962 and 1968?
9. Which two women provided vocals for the pop group The New Seekers?
10. Which Parisian-born artist painted *Vision After The Sermon* and at the time of his death was living on the island of Tahiti?

QUIZ SIX

1. At which sporting venue can spectators watch the action from the Paddock Hill Grandstand?

2. Who composed the theme music for the Australian TV soap *Neighbours*?

3. Which singer asked the question, 'Is this the way to Amarillo'?

4. Which murderer played on film by Richard Attenborough lived at 10 Rillington Place?

5. Who won a Best Actor Oscar for his role as Rooster Cogburn?

6. What is the secret identity of Batman?

7. Eric Clapton, Ginger Baker and which other rock star made up the trio Cream?

8. Who killed Lee Harvey Oswald?

9. Which Kenny Rogers hit opens with the line, 'You painted up your lips and curled your tindered hair'?

10. Jean Paget is the lead character in which novel by Nevil Shute?

QUIZ SEVEN

1. Who played Brian in the film *The Life Of Brian*?

2. Which evangelist once said, 'There is nothing in The Bible that says I must wear rags'?

3. Which singer had a worldwide hit in 1992 with 'Achy Breaky Heart'?

4. Who assassinated Martin Luther King?

5. Who replaced Captain Christopher Pike in a popular TV series?

6. Which actor was born Issur Demsky Danielovitch?

7. *The Way The Wind Blows* was the title of the memoirs of which former British Prime Minister?

8. Which star of the film *The Hunt For Red October* married Kim Basinger?

9. Who was British Prime Minister during the General Strike of the 1920s?

10. Who directed the film *Spartacus*?

QUIZ EIGHT

1. What has been won in past years by a Russian Hero, a Battleship and a Wild Man From Borneo?

2. Which waterway leaves the River Thames at Brentford, climbing over 50 locks into the Chiltern Hills?

3. What did the British parliament introduce as the national flag in 1905?

4. Who played the title role in the TV series *Dixon of Dock Green*?

5. Which film studio was founded in 1923 by four siblings called Sam, Jack, Harry and Albert?

6. Which album by Dire Straits was the first CD to sell a million in the UK?

7. Which play by George Bernard Shaw was set in war-torn Bulgaria?

8. Ronaldsway Airport serves which island?

9. What is the name of the most southerly island in the Shetland group that gives its name to a style of knitwear?

10. Which novel by William Makepeace Thackeray features the Osborne family and the Crawley family?

QUIZ NINE

1. Who played the role of William Thatcher in the film *A Knight's Tale*?

2. What was the original name of Manchester United FC?

3. Who connects the films *Grease* and *Xanadu*?

4. What are the names of the three members of the Darling family who accompanied Peter Pan to Never Never Land?

5. Whose 1991 album *Time Love And Tenderness* earned him a Grammy Award?

6. Which two teams contested the first FA Cup final to be played at Wembley?

7. What became an American state on June 20, 1863?

8. Which 1966 film co-starred Richard Burton, Elizabeth Taylor, George Segal and Sandy Dennis?

9. What was the title of the 1987 film in which Madonna co-starred alongside John Mills?

10. What was the title of the Robert Graves autobiography that chronicled his time in the World War I trenches on the Western Front?

QUIZ TEN

1. What name was given to the skeleton of early man found near Dusseldorf in 1856 and named after the valley where it was discovered?

2. Which children's book, which featured the green people of Gorm, was written by Prince Charles?

3. Mungo Jerry, Grizabella and Shimbleshanks are all the names of felines in which TS Eliot works?

4. Which novel featured a bat called Mang and a mongoose called Rikki-Tikki-Tavi?

5. In which film was Brendan Fraser found living in the wild with an elephant called Shep?

6. Who scored the second goal for Manchester United in the 1968 European Cup final?

7. In which 1997 film did Cameron Diaz and Julia Roberts play love rivals?

8. Which Lennon and McCartney composition was used as the theme song for the TV series *The Wonder Years*?

9. Alec Leamas is the lead character in which espionage novel penned by John Le Carre?

10. Aimless, Feckless, Graceless and Pointless are the names of cows in which novel?

QUIZ ONE

1. Which film starring Tom Hanks featured a pop group called The Wonders?
2. What song was a worldwide chart-topper for Sonny & Cher in 1965?
3. What was the title of the 1998 film sequel to *Babe*?
4. With which two clubs did Stanley Matthews play league football?
5. What building on the Lancashire coast was first opened to the public in May 1894?
6. In which building in the capital of England does the Ceremony of the Keys take place every night?
7. Which hit record for Ralph McTell opens with the line, 'Have you seen the old man in the closed down market'?
8. In which American crime TV series did Detective Mike Stone partner Detective Steve Keller?
9. What is the name of the Texan town where the Alamo stands?
10. Who married Melanie Griffith in 1995?

QUIZ TWO

1. What was moved from England to Lake Havasu City in Arizona in the 1960s?
2. Rick Baker won a Best Makeup Oscar for which lycanthrope movie directed by John Landis?
3. In which film did Kevin Spacey play the character of Lester Burnham?
4. Which equine literary character shared his home with Ginger and Merrylegs?
5. Which 2001 film told the true story of the Battle of Mogadishu?
6. What was the title of the 1983 No 1 hit of the Australian pop group Men At Work?
7. In which Jules Verne novel did Captain Nemo skipper the *Nautilus* submarine?
8. What is the world's largest sea?
9. In which Disney film did Uncle Remus tell tales about Brer Rabbit?
10. What is the title of the national anthem of Ireland?

QUIZ THREE

1. Who played Batman in the 1960s TV series?

2. Name the four American states that begin with the letter W.

3. Who wrote the novel *The Legend Of Sleepy Hollow*?

4. Who was the first ever actor to receive a knighthood?

5. In a TV comedy series, who played the role of Gareth Blackstock?

6. Which controversial comedian was portrayed by Dustin Hoffman in a 1974 film?

7. Who connects the films *Blind Date*, *Hudson Hawk* and *The Sixth Sense*?

8. Which former England cricket captain adopted the middle name of Dylan as a tribute to his musical hero Bob Dylan?

9. Name the two male stars that appeared in the series of Road films including *Road To Zanzibar* and *Road To Utopia*.

10. What is the name of the character played by Matthew Perry in the TV comedy *Friends*?

ANSWERS

1. Adam West 2. WEST Virginia, Washington, Wyoming and Wisconsin 3. WASHINGTON Irving 4. Sir Henry IRVING 5. Lenny HENRY 6. LENNY Bruce 7. BRUCE Willis 8. Bob WILLIS 9. BOB Hope and Bing Crosby 10. Chandler BING

QUIZ FOUR

1. What is the name of the accident-prone character played by Michael Crawford in *Some Mothers Do Ave Em*?
2. Who was the first actor to receive Best Actor Oscars in consecutive years?
3. Who piloted *Thunderbird One*?
4. Name the three members of the pop trio The Walker Brothers.
5. Who won the FA Cup in 1972?
6. What do the initials UNESCO stand for?
7. With its headquarters in Geneva, what do the initials WHO stand for?
8. In which Bond film did Robert Carlyle play a villain called Renard?
9. Pamela Stephenson, Rowan Atkinson, Mel Smith and Griff Rhys Jones appeared together in which TV comedy sketch show?
10. In the media world, what do the initials CNN stand for?

ANSWERS
1. Frank Spencer 2. SPENCER Tracy 3. Scott TRACY 4. SCOTT Engel, Gary Leeds and John Maus 5. LEEDS United 6. UNITED Nations Educational Scientific and Cultural Organisation 7. World Health ORGANISATION 8. The WORLD is Not Enough 9. NOT The Nine O'clock News 10. Cable NEWS Network

QUIZ FIVE

1. What name is given to the annual grant of money by Parliament to the monarch and other members of the Royal Family?
2. Which European conflict began in July 1936 and ended in April 1939?
3. The Battle of Bosworth Field and the Battle of Hexham were both fought during which war?
4. Slash, Steven, Duff, Izzy and Axl were the five members of which rock band?
5. In which 1988 film did Emilio Estevez play Billy the Kid?
6. Which male singer won the 2001 TV Pop Idol contest in the UK?
7. What is the title of the stage musical that opened in 2002 that features the music of the pop group Queen?
8. Which Hollywood superstar played the role of Daniel Reece in the TV soap *Dynasty*?
9. On which two rivers does the city of New York stand?
10. Which novel by John Steinbeck was adapted into a film starring James Dean?

QUIZ SIX

1. What barrier between England and Wales was built in the 8th century on the orders of the King of Mercia?

2. On film, which actor danced with animated penguins and Mary Poppins?

3. Which composer born in 1770 had his life story chronicled in the film *Immortal Beloved*?

4. Which Chuck Berry song was a hit for The Electric Light Orchestra in 1973?

5. Which legendary American jazz musician recorded 'The Black Bottom Stomp' in the 1920s?

6. Who wrote the book *Diana, Her True Story*?

7. Which American singer had hits with 'Never Let Her Slip Away' and 'Lonely Boy'?

8. What was the country of Ghana called before March 1957?

9. According to the song 'American Pie' what was caught by the Father, the Son and the Holy Ghost?

10. Uncas, Hawkeye and Chingachgook are all characters in which novel by James Fenimore Cooper?

ANSWERS

1. Offa's Dyke 2. Dick Van DYKE 3. Ludwig VAN Beethoven 4. 'Roll Over BEETHOVEN' 5. Jelly ROLL Morton 6. Andrew MORTON 7. ANDREW Gold 8. The GOLD Coast 9. The Last Train For The COAST 10. LAST Of The Mohicans

QUIZ SEVEN

1. Which stage musical set in the 1920s tells the story of a chorus girl called Roxy Hart?
2. Which American football team won the Super Bowl in 1986?
3. Which popular fairytale features three ursine characters and a golden-haired girl?
4. In the nursery rhyme, who ran after the farmer's wife?
5. George Milton and Lennie Small are the main characters in which novel by John Steinbeck?
6. Which film directed by Leonard Nimoy featured an architect called Peter, an actor called Jack and a cartoonist called Michael?
7. Which Rod Stewart hit featured on the album *Body Wishes* and contains the line, 'Now you're moving in high society'?
8. What was the real name of Calamity Jane?
9. In which film did Bob Hope play a character called Wally Campbell?
10. Which singer changed his name to Yusuf Islam?

QUIZ EIGHT

1. Who did Sirhan Sirhan assassinate in June 1968?
2. Who wrote the poems *The Jolly Beggars* and *To A Mouse*?
3. Who was the lead vocalist with the 80s pop group Dead Or Alive?
4. Who played lead guitar for the rock group The Who?
5. Who created the literary character of Adrian Mole?
6. Who did the singer Dion advise you to stay away from?
7. In which 1999 film did Julia Roberts eventually marry Richard Gere?
8. What was the title of the 1950 film in which Elizabeth Taylor played the daughter of Spencer Tracy?
9. What title is given to the MP with the longest unbroken service in the House of Commons?
10. What did David Lloyd George refer to as 'Mr Balfour's poodle'?

ANSWERS

1. Robert Kennedy 2. ROBERT Burns 3. Pete BURNS 4. PETE Townsend 5. Sue TOWNSEND 6. 'Runaround SUE' 7. *RUNaway Bride* 8. *Father of the BRIDE* 9. FATHER Of The House 10. HOUSE Of Lords

QUIZ NINE

1. Which 80s band had hits with 'Only You', 'When You're Young And In Love' and 'Who's That Girl'?

2. Which 1965 film comedy was set in 1919 and told the story of a race across the English Channel for a £10,000 prize?

3. How are Britt, Lee, Vin, O'Reilly, Chris, Harry and Chico collectively known in the title of a film?

4. Which musical set on an Oregon ranch featured Howard Keel playing the character of Adam Pontabee?

5. Which pop trio had hits with 'The Sun Ain't Gonna Shine Anymore' and 'Make It Easy On Yourself'?

6. Which sports commentator once observed 'Ralf Schumacher has been upstaged by the young teenager Jensen Button, who is twenty'?

7. Which 50s singing star had hits with 'Softly, Softly' and 'Heartbeat'?

8. Which three actresses shared a flat with Tracey Ullman in the sitcom *Girls On Top*?

9. What are the six official languages of the United Nations?

10. Which novel by Michael Ondaatje won the Booker Prize in 1992 and went on to become an Oscar-winning movie?

QUIZ TEN

1. What was the title of the Grammy-winning album by Stevie Wonder that contained the tracks 'Isn't She Lovely' and 'Sir Duke'?

2. Which biographical TV programme saw Michael Aspel replacing Eamon Andrews as the presenter?

3. What was the title of the only top 20 hit in the UK for the American vocal duo, James and Bobby Purify?

4. With which song did Sandie Shaw win the Eurovision Song Contest?

5. Which piece of classical music composed by J S Bach has been used to advertise Hamlet cigars on TV?

6. What is the official name of the US Presidential plane?

7. Which novel by Ken Kesey was adapted into an Oscar-winning film starring Jack Nicholson?

8. Which song from the film *The Wizard Of Oz* won a Best Song Oscar?

9. What was the name of the flagship of the Greenpeace organisation that was sunk by two bombs in July 1985?

10. What was the title of the 1999 film in which Antonio Banderas played a 10th-century Arab ambassador called Ahmed Ibn Fadlan?

ANSWERS
1. Songs In The Key Of Life 2. This Is Your LIFE 3. 'I'm YOUR Puppet' 4. 'PUPPET On A String' 5. Air On A G STRING 6. AIR Force One 7. ONE Flew Over The Cuckoos Nest 8. 'OVER The Rainbow' 9. RAINBOW Warrior 10. The 13th WARRIOR

QUIZ ONE

1. What does a cooper make for a living?

2. Which film directed by Guy Ritchie featured Vinnie Jones as Big Chris Sting?

3. Speed, Lucetta, Panthino and Julia are all characters in which Shakespeare play?

4. The songs 'Bye Bye Baby' and 'Diamonds Are A Girl's Best Friend' featured in which film?

5. Linda Perry was the lead vocalist for which US all-girl pop group?

6. What is the collective name for War, Death, Famine and Pestilence?

7. Marlon Brando played Colonel Kurtz in which film?

8. Which disco hit by Jimmy James and the Vagabonds contains the line, 'Revolution is no solution'?

9. What was the title of the 60s American TV show that featured two scientists called Tony Newman and Doug Phillips?

10. Which 20km-long structure was completed in 1905 and connects Italy to Switzerland?

QUIZ TWO

1. Whose face is said to have launched a thousand ships?

2. Who wrote the novel *Bridget Jones's Diary*?

3. Who wrote the novel *The History Of Tom Jones, A Foundling*?

4. Name the four British boxers who fought Muhammad Ali.

5. Who played the husband of Grace Kelly in the film *High Noon*?

6. Which Manchester United defender was forced to pull out of England's 2002 World Cup squad due to a broken metatarsal?

7. Who was appointed Lord Mayor of Birmingham in 1915 and 22 years later became Prime Minister of Great Britain?

8. Who played Alan Quartermain on film and Dr Kildare on TV?

9. Which film star couple married for the first time in 1964 in Canada and for the second time in Africa in 1975?

10. Who wrote the novel *A Woman Of Substance*?

ANSWERS

1. Helen of Troy 2. HELEN Fielding 3. Henry FIELDING 4. HENRY Cooper, Brian London, Richard Dunn and Joe Bugner 5. Gary COOPER 6. GARY Neville 7. NEVILLE Chamberlain 8. Richard CHAMBERLAIN 9. Elizabeth Taylor and RICHARD Burton 10. Barbara TAYLOR Bradford

7

QUIZ THREE

1. In which film did Harrison Ford play a cop called John Book?
2. What is the title of the TV drama in which Amanda Burton plays a pathologist called Samantha Ryan?
3. Which popular Christmas carol was written by an Austrian priest called Joseph Mohr?
4. What was the only UK chart hit of the 20th century that featured the vocals of Michael Crawford?
5. Which classical piece of music was composed by George Frederic Handel in 1740 for a boating party of King George I?
6. Which novel by Gavin Maxwell tells the story of an otter called Mij?
7. Which song written by Mike Batt featured in the film *Watership Down* and provided a huge hit for Art Garfunkel?
8. What was the title of the 1978 film thriller in which Faye Dunaway starred as a fashion photographer with psychic powers?
9. Who did Sheryl Lee play in the cult TV series *Twin Peaks*?
10. Which singer was addicted to love and claimed that some guys have all the luck?

ANSWERS

1. *Witness* 2. *Silent WITNESS* 3. 'SILENT Night' 4. 'Music Of The NIGHT' 5. *The Water MUSIC* 6. *Ring Of Bright WATER* 7. 'BRIGHT Eyes' 8. *The EYES Of Laura Mars* 9. LAURA Palmer 10. Robert PALMER

QUIZ FOUR

1. Which song from the musical *Porgy and Bess* mentions in the lyrics the biblical characters of David, Goliath, Jonah and Moses?

2. In which TV sitcom did Windsor Davies play Sergeant Major Williams?

3. Which film musical starring Tommy Steele featured the song 'Flash Bang Wallop'?

4. What was the title of the Somerset Maugham novel written in 1919 and based on the life of the painter Paul Gaugin?

5. The Last Message Cavor Sent To Earth is the final chapter in which novel by HG Wells?

6. In which film did Henry Fonda play Juror No 8?

7. Cleaning the stables of King Augeas, capturing the Cretan Bull and retrieving the belt of Hippolyte were three of the what?

8. Which Shakespeare play features the characters of Ferdinand, Longaville and Biron?

9. Which 1960s sci-fi TV show featured the adventures of the Robinson family?

10. What was the title of the film in which Dennis Quaid was shrunk and injected into the body of Meg Ryan?

ANSWERS

1. 'It Ain't Necessarily So'. 2. It AIN'T Half Hot Mum 3. HALF A Sixpence 4. The Moon And SIXPENCE 5. The First Men In The MOON 6. Twelve Angry MEN 7. The TWELVE Labours of Hercules 8. Love's LABOURS Lost 9. LOST In Space 10. Inner SPACE

QUIZ FIVE

1. Which golfing trophy is contested by women's amateur teams from the USA and Great Britain?

2. On film, who has played The Boston Strangler and Harry Houdini?

3. Who is the father-in-law of Tony Blair?

4. Who assassinated an American President at Ford's Theatre?

5. Who duetted on the 1976 hit record 'Don't Go Breaking My Heart'?

6. Who played Dorothy in the film *Gregory's Girl*?

7. Who played Eliza Doolittle and Henry Higgins in the 1964 film musical *My Fair Lady*?

8. What was the name of the character played by Penelope Keith in the TV sitcom *To The Manor Born*?

9. Which daughter of Nanette Newman followed her mother into the world of showbusiness?

10. Who has been played on film by Uma Thurman and on TV by Diana Rigg?

ANSWERS

1. The Curtis Cup 2. Tony CURTIS 3. TONY Booth 4. John Wilkes BOOTH 5. Elton JOHN & Kiki Dee 6. DEE Hepburn 7. Audrey HEPBURN & Rex Harrison 8. AUDREY Forbes Hamilton 9. Emma FORBES 10. EMMA Peel

QUIZ SIX

1. Which of Hitler's henchmen was born in the village of Bad Godesberg in 1913 and was put on trial in 1987 for his crimes against humanity?

2. Manufactured by Mattel, what is the name of the world's best-selling doll and what is the name of her boyfriend?

3. Who was elected Mayor of London in May 2000?

4. A statue of which explorer stands next to the Victoria Falls in Africa?

5. In which 1954 film comedy did Dirk Bogarde play Dr Simon Sparrow?

6. In which 2000 film did Martin Lawrence play an FBI agent called Malcolm Turner who disguised himself as a grandmother to catch an escaped convict?

7. What was the title of the television drama set in the 1870s, in which Barbara Stanwyck played the head of the Barkley family?

8. What was the title of the 1966 novel by Jacqueline Susann that became one of the world's best-selling books?

9. Which dolls, created by Xavier Roberts, came complete with adoption forms?

10. In which 1998 film directed by Tom Shadyac did Robin Williams play an unconventional doctor?

ANSWERS

1. Klaus Barbie 2. BARBIE & Ken 3. KEN Livingstone 4. Dr LIVINGSTONE 5. DR In The House 6. Big Momma's HOUSE 7. The BIG Valley 8. VALLEY Of The Dolls 9. Cabbage Patch DOLLS 10. PATCH Adams

QUIZ SEVEN

1. Which statue, one of the seven wonders of the ancient world, stood on the second largest Greek island?
2. Who founded the De Beers Mining Company in South Africa?
3. Which Conservative minister resigned from Margaret Thatcher's cabinet following an affair with his secretary Sarah Keays?
4. Which chat-show host is affectionately known as Parky?
5. Who collaborated on the hit single 'I Knew You Were Waiting'?
6. Which statesman invented bifocals, the rocking chair and the lightning rod?
7. Which doctor published a book called *Baby And Child Care* in 1946?
8. What was the full title of the third film that features the crew of the USS *Enterprise*?
9. By what name is the heavenly body Sirius also known?
10. 'I'm The Urban Spaceman' was the biggest hit record for which 1960s band led by Neil Innes?

QUIZ EIGHT

1. What is the official residence of the Lord Mayor of London?
2. Queen Anne, James I, James II, Charles I and Charles II were all members of which royal house?
3. In which 1999 film did Nathan Lane provide the voice of a cat called Snowbell?
4. Which nursery rhyme character sat among the cinders?
5. Who played Beryl and Sandra in the TV sitcom *The Liver Birds*?
6. Which British actor played Erwin Rommel in the 1951 film *The Desert Fox*?
7. What name was given to the boundary in the USA that in the 1760s separated Maryland and Pennsylvania?
8. Which 1998 film set in World War II boasted an impressive cast that included John Travolta, George Clooney, Sean Penn and Nick Nolte?
9. Which farmyard bird provided The Rolling Stones with a 1964 chart-topper?
10. What was the name of the character played by John Wayne in the Oscar-winning film *True Grit*?

QUIZ NINE

1. What is the official residence of the Archbishop of Canterbury?
2. Which building, on which construction began in 1514, was presented to Henry VIII by Cardinal Wolsey?
3. What is the name of the island of Sark's parliament?
4. Which piece of music originally created for a stage adaptation of a Sir Walter Scott poem, *The Lady of the Lake*, is today played to greet the arrival of the American President?
5. Name the four types of weather that are classed as precipitation.
6. Which Carol King hit contains the line, 'The weather here has been as nice as it can be'?
7. What was the name of the terrorist group responsible for the massacre of eleven Israeli athletes at the 1972 Olympics?
8. In which Alan Bleasdale drama did Bernard Hill play Yosser Hughes?
9. What was the title of the 1987 film in which Kiefer Sutherland played the leader of a group of rampaging vampires?
10. What novel by James Hilton was set in the mythical land of Shangri-la?

QUIZ TEN

1. Which novel featured a horse called Boxer and a pig called Napoleon?

2. Which US rock band had a 2001 trans-Atlantic hit with a cover version of the Michael Jackson song 'Smooth Criminal'?

3. What was the title of the 1988 film in which Kim Basinger played an extraterrestrial spy called Celeste?

4. Which novel by Richard Llewelyn told the story of the Morgan family who lived in a Welsh mining village?

5. What are the names of the three male murder suspects in the board game of Cluedo?

6. In the cartoon series *Wacky Races* who drove the Convert-A-Car?

7. Who was Men's Singles Champion at Wimbledon in 1987?

8. Which country and western star recorded live albums at Folsom Prison and San Quentin Prison?

9. Which 1960s pop group was formed by Frederick Heath after he took to wearing an eye patch?

10. Which Gilbert & Sullivan opera is sub-titled The Slave Of Duty?

ANSWERS

1. *Animal Farm* 2. Alien Ant FARM 3. *My Stepmother Is An ALIEN* 4. *How Green Was My Valley* 5. Reverend GREEN, Professor Plum, Colonel Mustard 6. PROFESSOR Pat Pending 7. PAT Cash 8. Johnny CASH 9. JOHNNY Kidd And The Pirates 10. *The PIRATES Of Penzance*

SESSION 8

QUIZ ONE

1. What is the capital of Trinidad & Tobago?
2. Which city stands at the northern end of the Suez Canal?
3. Which pop group was formed by the Fairbrass brothers, Richard and Craig?
4. Which Hollywood dancing partners co-starred in the films *The Gay Divorcee* and *Follow The Fleet*?
5. What were the five 'spice' names of the Spice Girls?
6. Which Chicago gangster was born Lester Joseph Gillis?
7. What 1993 film saw the directorial debut of Mel Gibson?
8. What do the initials AWOL stand for?
9. What was the title of the 1961 film that saw the creation of a new resilient flying rubber dubbed Flubber?
10. In the Gerry Anderson TV series, who invented Supercar?

QUIZ TWO

1. Which Puccini opera features the characters of Rodolfo and Mimi?

2. What was composed by Dale Wasserman as a musical version of the story of Don Quixote?

3. In which classic film did Orson Welles play the character of Harry Lime?

4. Which Spielberg blockbuster climaxed with Richard Dreyfuss leaving Earth on an alien spacecraft?

5. In which film did Alec Guinness play eight members of the d'Ascoyne family?

6. Which monarch shouted 'off with her head' in the novel *Alice's Adventures In Wonderland*?

7. Which monarch rode a horse called Black Agnes?

8. Who wrote the novel *Frankenstein*?

9. Which film star was born Shirley Schrift?

10. Leontes, the King of Sicily, features in which play by William Shakespeare?

ANSWERS

1. *La Boheme* 2. *Man of LA Mancha* 3. *The Third MAN* 4. *Close Encounters of the THIRD Kind* 5. *KIND Hearts And Coronets* 6. The Queen of HEARTS 7. Mary QUEEN Of Scots 8. MARY Shelley 9. SHELLEY Winters 10. *The WINTER'S Tale*

QUIZ THREE

1. Which British entertainer was born Michael Dumble Smith?

2. Who won an Oscar for his role in the film *All The King's Men* and went on to star in the TV series *Highway Patrol*?

3. Which star of the film *Inspector Gadget* is married to *Sex In The City* star Sarah Jessica Parker?

4. Name the four men who wrote the Gospels in the New Testament?

5. Who played the title role in the 1980 film *The Elephant Man*?

6. What was the first No 1 single for the 80s pop group Culture Club?

7. In which film did Mel Gibson play Nick Marshall and Helen Hunt play Darcy McGuire?

8. What was the title of the 1987 hit on which the Pet Shop Boys collaborated with Dusty Springfield?

9. What was the title of the first Mickey Spillane novel to feature the character of Mike Hammer?

10. Which TV record review show has been hosted by David Jacobs, Noel Edmonds and Jools Holland?

ANSWERS

1. Michael Crawford 2. Broderick CRAWFORD 3. Matthew BRODERICK
4. MATTHEW, Mark, Luke and John 5. JOHN Hurt 6. 'Do You Really Want To HURT Me?'
7. *What Women WANT* 8. 'WHAT Have I Done To Deserve This' 9. *I The Jury*
10. *Juke Box JURY*

QUIZ FOUR

1. Who won an Oscar for his role as a gifted pianist in the film *Shine*?

2. Who played the married couple Ria and Ben Parkinson in the Carla Lane sitcom *Butterflies*?

3. Whose debut single 'Fill Me In' and debut album, *Born To Do It* both stormed to the top of the charts?

4. Which member of the Partridge Family had solo hits with 'Daydreamer' and 'How Can I Be Sure'?

5. Which classic western film told the true story of Robert Leroy Parker and Henry Longbaugh?

6. Who did Pete Duel and Ben Murphy play in the TV series *Alias Smith and Jones*?

7. Who did George Peppard play in the *A Team*?

8. Which sport star's autobiography is entitled *V Is For Victory*?

9. Which scientist is credited with the discovery of the circulation of the blood?

10. Who wrote the novel *Lord Of The Flies*?

QUIZ FIVE

1. Which American soul star composed the music for the film *Shaft*?

2. Which Lincolnshire-born scientist discovered the theory of gravity?

3. Who played the role of Sandy in the film musical *Grease*?

4. Who was the second President of the USA?

5. Which pop star is married to the footballer that captained England's World Cup team in 2002?

6. Who wrote and starred as Brenda in the TV sitcom *Dinnerladies*?

7. Which conductor, born in 1869, was a co-founder of the Promenade Concerts?

8. Who wrote the novel *The Bostonians*?

9. Which soul legend sang 'Living In America' in the film *Rocky IV*?

10. What is the name of the clerical sleuth created by GK Chesterton?

ANSWERS

1. Isaac Hayes 2. Sir ISAAC Newton 3. Olivia NEWTON John 4. JOHN Adams 5. Victoria ADAMS 6. VICTORIA Wood 7. Sir Henry WOOD 8. HENRY James 9. JAMES Brown 10. Father BROWN

QUIZ SIX

1. Au is the chemical symbol for which precious metal?
2. What name was given to the 1520 meeting place of Henry VIII and Francis III, who met for the purpose of arranging an alliance?
3. Who won Best Actress Oscars for her roles in the films *Norma Rae* and *Places In The Heart*?
4. Which song written by Buddy Rice has been recorded by Wilson Pickett, The Commitments and Buddy Guy?
5. What make of car did Steve McQueen drive in the film *Bullitt*?
6. Who played the husband of Michelle Pfeiffer in the film *What Lies Beneath*?
7. Which member of The Beatles died in a Los Angeles hospital in November 2001?
8. The heads of which four American Presidents are depicted on Mount Rushmore?
9. Which gap-toothed actor links the films *How To Murder Your Wife* and *Blue Murder At St Trinians*?
10. Who wrote a series of futuristic novels entitled *Discworld*?

ANSWERS

1. Gold 2. The Field of the Cloth Of GOLD 3. Sally FIELD 4. "Mustang SALLY" 5. Ford MUSTANG 6. Harrison FORD 7. George HARRISON 8. GEORGE Washington, Theodore Roosevelt, Abraham Lincoln and Thomas Jefferson 9. Terry THOMAS 10. TERRY Pratchett

QUIZ SEVEN

1. Which 1954 winner of the Nobel Prize for Literature died in 1961 from self-inflicted gunshot wounds?

2. Who won the Nobel Prize for Chemistry in 1908 and was knighted in 1914?

3. When the pop group Genesis released the album *And Then There Were Three*, who were the three members?

4. Which England goalkeeper made a 'wonder save' from a Pele header in a 1970 World Cup match?

5. Which military leader was born in 1833 and died at Khartoum in 1885?

6. Which singer played the music shop owner in the film *The Blues Brothers*?

7. What was the title of the 1998 album by Madonna on which she collaborated with the record producer William Orbit?

8. Which poem that chronicled an historical event contains the line, 'All in the valley of death rode the six hundred'?

9. Vicki Brown provided the female vocals on which 1976 chart-topping single by J J Barrie?

10. In which film did Bernard Lee first play the role of M?

QUIZ EIGHT

1. Nashville is the capital of which American state?

2. Who wrote the plays *The Glass Menagerie* and *The Night Of The Iguana*?

3. Who links the films *The Fisher King* and *The Birdcage*?

4. What are the first names of the Gibb brothers in the Bee Gees?

5. Who composed the themes for the Bond films *Goldfinger* and *Thunderball*?

6. Born on May 18, 1920, how is Karol Josef Wojtyla better known?

7. Which British author penned the poems *The Rape Of The Lock* and *The Dunciad*?

8. Which inventor was born in Edinburgh on March 3, 1847?

9. Which ex-Arsenal manager was nicknamed Stroller in his playing days?

10. Who was governor of Texas from 1994 to 2000?

ANSWERS

1. Tennessee   2. TENNESSEE Williams   3. Robin WILLIAMS   4. ROBIN, Barry and Maurice
5. John BARRY   6. Pope JOHN Paul II   7. Alexander POPE   8. ALEXANDER Graham Bell
9. George GRAHAM   10. GEORGE W Bush

QUIZ NINE

1. Who was the fourth wife of Peter Sellers?

2. Who wrote the novel *The Odessa File*?

3. Who provided the voice of Charlie in the TV series *Charlie's Angels*?

4. Which Duke was born Marion Morrison?

5. What were the character names of 'The Magnificent Seven' in the first TV series of *Auf Wiedersehen Pet*?

6. In World War II, what type of plane was used in the Dam Busters raid?

7. What is the London address of the Football Association?

8. Which song has been a hit for Ringo Starr and Johnny Burnette?

9. In which award-winning film does Russell Crowe play the Nobel Prize winner John Nash?

10. What was the title of the 70s TV British sitcom in which Barry Evans played an English teacher whose class comprised entirely of foreign students?

ANSWERS

1. Lynne Frederick 2. FREDERICK Forsyth 3. John FORSYTH 4. JOHN Wayne 5. WAYNE, Neville, Bomber, Oz, Dennis, Barry and Moxy 6. The Lancaster BOMBER 7. 16 LANCASTER Gate 8. 'You're 16, You're Beautiful and You're Mine' 9. A BEAUTIFUL Mind 10. MIND Your Language

QUIZ TEN

1. According to the song, where did the Shangri-Las meet the leader of the pack?

2. Who played the coach of a Jamaican bobsleigh team in the film *Cool Runnings*?

3. Who was photographed kissing the toes of Sarah Ferguson in 1992?

4. Which three pop superstars collaborated on the 1994 song 'All For Love'?

5. Which actor connects Captain Ahab and Captain Jean Luc Piccard?

6. Name the first two men to play Dr Who on TV.

7. Who was known as Lord Haw Haw during World War II?

8. Which Irish author's controversial novel *Ulysses* was first published in 1922?

9. Which brothers from America's Wild West led the Quantrill Gang?

10. Which rock star was backed by The Mothers Of Invention?

ANSWERS

1. At the candy store 2. John CANDY 3. JOHN Bryan 4. BRYAN Adams, Rod Stewart and Sting 5. Patrick STEWART 6. William Hartnell and PATRICK Troughton 7. WILLIAM Joyce 8. James JOYCE 9. Frank & Jesse JAMES 10. FRANK Zappa

SESSION 9

QUIZ ONE

1. What is the capital of Cuba?
2. Which novel by Graham Greene featured a vacuum cleaner representative called Wormold?
3. What was the title of Kate Bush's follow-up single to 'Wuthering Heights'?
4. In which 1986 film did Eddie Murphy find himself protecting an infant with special powers?
5. Which sacred Sikh building is also known as Darbar Sahib?
6. What was the title of the first film sequel to *Raiders of the Lost Ark*?
7. Which singer played himself in the film *Mars Attacks*?
8. In the nursery rhyme, who stole a pig and ran away?
9. What did my true love give to me on the eleventh day of Christmas?
10. Which murder weapon in the board game of Cluedo would you associate with the chemical symbol Pb?

QUIZ TWO

1. What is the title of the stage musical that tells the story of Manchester United and opened with Russell Watson playing Sir Matt Busby?

2. In which 1989 film did Kevin Costner play a farmer from Iowa who builds a baseball pitch?

3. Which British actress was born Shirley Broomfield in 1938?

4. What was the title of the novel that was a follow-up to *Anne of Green Gables*?

5. What is the meteorological nickname of Chicago?

6. In which 1984 film did Clint Eastwood play Lieutenant Spear?

7. *They Call Me Mr Tibbs* was the film sequel to which 1967 film starring Sidney Poitier?

8. Which 1977 film featured the songs, 'You Should Be Dancing' and 'More Than A Woman'?

9. What is the alternative name for the disease Scarlatina?

10. In which novel by Nathaniel Hawthorne is the central character called Hester Prynne?

ANSWERS

1. *Theatre of Dreams* 2. *Field Of DREAMS* 3. Shirley Anne FIELD 4. ANNE Of Windy Poplars 5. The WINDY City 6. *CITY Heat* 7. *In the HEAT Of The Night* 8. *Saturday NIGHT Fever* 9. Scarlet FEVER 10. *The SCARLET Letter*

QUIZ THREE

1. Which American TV soap told the story of the Gioberti family and the Channing family?
2. Which Antarctic explorer received a posthumous knighthood after his death in 1912?
3. What are the names of the five Tracy brothers in *Thunderbirds*?
4. Who played Gregory in the film *Gregory's Girl*?
5. Which West Ham footballer was a last-minute replacement for Danny Murphy in England's 2002 World Cup squad?
6. When Marlon Brando played Fletcher Christian, who played Captain Bligh?
7. Who played the Roman slave Lurcio in the 70s TV comedy series *Up Pompeii*?
8. Which Liverpool pop group had hits with the songs 'Two Tribes' and 'The Power Of Love'?
9. What was the best-selling song of the pop group Edison Lighthouse?
10. Name the singer who died in 2002 who recorded the original version of 'This Ole House'?

QUIZ FOUR

1. Which Olympic skier married Chris Evert Lloyd in 1987?
2. Which novel by George Eliot told the story of the Tulliver family?
3. In which 1971 film comedy did Bill Maynard play Guy Fawkes?
4. Which two monarchs led the opposing forces in The Battle Of Bosworth Field?
5. Which classical composer was born in Leipzig in May 1813 and died in Venice in February 1883?
6. Who played the role of Jonathan Hart on TV?
7. In the TV sitcom *I Spy* who played the spies, Alexander Scott and Kelly Robertson?
8. Which children's characters live in flowerpots and speak their own language called Oddle-poddle?
9. Which Oscar-winning actor was born Krishna Banji?
10. Who wrote the novels *The Old Devils* and *Colonel Sun*?

ANSWERS

1. Andy Mill 2. MILL on the Floss 3. Carry ON Henry 4. HENRY VII & Richard III 5. RICHARD Wagner 6. Robert WAGNER 7. ROBERT Culp & Bill Cosby 8. BILL & Ben 9. BEN Kingsley 10. KINGSLEY Amis

QUIZ FIVE

1. Which film starring Meryl Streep recounted the true story of Lindy Chamberlain, whose baby was snatched by a dingo?
2. In which film did Denzel Washington play Steve Biko?
3. What was the title of the 1994 autobiography of Nelson Mandela?
4. Which Lou Reed hit record starts with the line, 'Holly came from Miami FLA'?
5. In which film did William Holden play Pike Bishop, the leader of a gang of violent aging outlaws?
6. How are Mike, Carol, Jan, Alice, Cindy, Greg, Peter and Bobby collectively known?
7. Which controversial prisoner published a book entitled *The Gates Of Janus: Serial Killing and Its Analysis*?
8. Which footballer broke the goal-scoring record of Cliff Bastin for Arsenal?
9. Which architect wrote the books *A Testament* and *The Story of the Tower*?
10. Who captained the West Indian cricket team to win the World Cup in 1975 and 1979?

ANSWERS
1. *A Cry In The Dark* 2. *CRY Freedom* 3. *The Long Walk To FREEDOM* 4. 'A WALK On The Wild Side' 5. *The WILD Bunch* 6. *The Brady BUNCH* 7. Ian BRADY 8. IAN Wright 9. Frank Lloyd WRIGHT 10. Clive LLOYD

QUIZ SIX

1. What is the capital of Bermuda?
2. Who met Horatio Nelson in 1793 and bore him a daughter called Horatia?
3. Which film had two versions made, the first in 1945 starring Margaret Lockwood and the second in 1983 starring Faye Dunaway?
4. Who did Dorothy's house fall on and kill in *The Wizard Of Oz*?
5. Zelda Spellman and Salem the cat are characters in which TV series?
6. What were the first names of the original three characters that made up Charlie's Angels?
7. Who married Prince Rainier of Monaco in 1956?
8. What was the name of the plucky heroine who helped to rescue survivors of the shipwrecked boat the *Forfarshire* in 1838?
9. Which H E Bates novel told the story of the Larkin family?
10. Who wrote the novel *Little Women*?

QUIZ SEVEN

1. Who were the first two men to set foot on the moon?

2. Which musician was nicknamed Satchmo, short for Satchel mouth?

3. What are the first four names of the eldest son of Prince Charles?

4. With what name was the horror movie actor Boris Karloff born?

5. What was the name of the character played by John Thaw in the TV sitcom *Home To Roost*?

6. Which Kenneth Grahame novel opens with the line, 'The Mole had been working very hard all the morning, spring cleaning his little home'?

7. Which Andrew Lloyd Webber musical features the songs 'When Children Rule The World' and 'No Matter What'?

8. Which 1992 film based on the best-selling novel of Fannie Flagg featured the characters of Ninny Threadgoode and Evelyn Couch?

9. The first Super Bowl in 1967 was won by which American football team?

10. Which Scottish pop group who sang 'Summer Love Sensation' were famed for wearing tartan clothing?

QUIZ EIGHT

1. What do the initials RAF stand for?
2. Which special armed unit, based on the SAS, was founded in the USA in November 1977?
3. What are the first four letters of the Greek alphabet?
4. What is the name of the North Sea oilrig where 167 workers were tragically killed in July 1988?
5. Which 35-year-old DJ and 18-year-old pop star married in Las Vegas in May 2001?
6. Who played Krystle Carrington in *Dynasty*?
7. Which husband and wife performed together on the albums *Back To The Egg* and *Band On The Run*?
8. Who played the title role in the film *Crocodile Dundee*?
9. Which star of the World Wrestling Federation fought Sylvester Stallone in the film *Rocky III*?
10. Who did Dr Banner turn into when he lost his temper?

ANSWERS

1. Royal Air Force 2. The Delta FORCE 3. Alpha, Beta, Omega and DELTA 4. Piper ALPHA 5. Billie PIPER & Chris Evans 6. Linda EVANS 7. LINDA & Paul McCartney 8. PAUL Hogan 9. Hulk HOGAN 10. The Incredible HULK

QUIZ NINE

1. Who played Inspector Dreyfus in the Pink Panther films?
2. Which British horror novelist wrote the books *Fluke*, *Survivor* and *The Rats*?
3. The TV series *Cor Blimey* told the story of the love affair between which two Carry On stars?
4. Which building dating from the Norman Conquest houses St George's Hall and The Queen's Private Chapel?
5. In which building did the investiture of Prince Charles as the Prince of Wales take place?
6. In November 1922 which two men unsealed the doors to the tomb of Tutankhamen?
7. Who directed the films *Cocoon* and *Backdraft*?
8. Who played Fagan in the Oscar-winning musical *Oliver*?
9. With which pop group did Justin Hayward record the album *On The Threshold Of A Dream*?
10. Which 1988 film based on a Neil Simon story starred Christopher Walken as Sergeant Toomey and Matthew Broderick as Eugene Morris Jerome?

ANSWERS

1. Herbert Lom 2. James HERBERT 3. Sid JAMES & Barbara Windsor 4. WINDSOR Castle 5. Caernavon CASTLE 6. Lord CARNARVON & Howard Carter 7. Ron HOWARD 8. RON Moody 9. The MOODY Blues 10. *Biloxi BLUES*

QUIZ TEN

1. Who was Clyde Barrow's female partner in crime?
2. Who directed the films *Fame* and *Midnight Express*?
3. Who was the youngest member of England's 1966 World Cup winning team?
4. At which event did the ants dance with the fleas whilst the worms squirmed?
5. Which American rock group released the album *Motel California* in 1996?
6. In which 1998 film did Bill Paxton co-star with a huge mountain gorilla?
7. Who left the Q Tips to have a solo hit with 'Wherever I Lay My Hat'?
8. Who played the lead roles of Johnny Hooker and Henry Gondorrf in an Oscar-winning film?
9. *Catriona*, a sequel to the novel *Kidnapped,* was written by which author?
10. In 1885 who successfully tested his first vaccine against rabies?

ANSWERS

1. Bonnie Parker 2. Alan PARKER 3. ALAN Ball 4. The Ugly Bug BALL 5. UGLY Kid Joe 6. *Mighty JOE Young* 7. Paul YOUNG 8. PAUL Newman & Robert Redford in *The Sting* 9. ROBERT Louis Stevenson 10. LOUIS Pasteur